THE GOSPEL ACCORD

The Gospel According to St Lynas

FRANK PAGDEN

MITRE
Tunbridge Wells

First published 1993

ISBN 1 85424 242 3

British Library Cataloguing-in-Publication Data.
A catalogue record for this book is available
from the British Library.

Produced by Bookprint Creative Services
P.O. Box 827, BN23 6NX, England for
Mitre, an imprint of Monarch Publications
P.O. Box 163, Tunbridge Wells, Kent TN3 0NX
Printed in England by Clays Ltd, St Ives plc

For Daniel, Kathryn, David, Matthew
and Simon

Introduction

St Lynas is a funny old fellow—really a throw-back to those awkward Celtic saints who caused St Augustine such headaches when he tried to bully them in the sixth century. Indeed the way St Lynas is losing his hair bears a resemblance to the peculiar haircuts they adopted—bald at the front, and too long at the rear.

He lives at the back of my mind, and in a small Christian community with some friends and young people who like him, are stimulated by what he says, and are tickled by his sense of humour. He tends to wear a cassock, not because he's a monk, but because he says it's a lot less trouble, you don't have to worry about your underwear, and you can get anything through the customs.

The things he says and gets up to were broadcast on BBC Ceefax, and they still appear on special occasions. He looks at them in wonder when they are on the screen and complains that I ought to have recorded what he MEANT, not what he said. In fact many of his sayings have an inner meaning and are worth exercising our ponder muscle on.

He reads all the books on my shelves. Like a squirrel he collects stories from Arabia, America, India, and the Jewish Talmud, meets all my friends, listens very critically to all I say, pinches my jokes, polishes it all up, and then passes it off as his own.

But I don't mind really. As we say in Yorkshire 'he can see through a closed door a bit further than most,' and in any case there's a group of us, Gladys, Jan, Rosemary, Colin, Stuart, and I, who are really rather fond of him. I hope that by the end of this book you'll feel the same.

Incidentally, his name is pronounced with a short 'i' as in St Linness, and if you say it quickly several times you'll get the drift.

FRANK PAGDEN

THE VOICE OF GOD

St Lynas was walking through the fields
one fresh sun-filled morning.

'You there God?' he enquired.
'Yup,' said God. (But it may have been a rook.)
'Wonderful world you've made,' commented St Lynas,
taking a deep breath.
'Inde-e-ed,' said God. (But it could have been a chaffinch.)
'Anything to say to me direct,
like heavenly voices and things?'
'Nope,' said God. (But of course it might have been a cow.)

JOY

A young lady after visiting St Lynas gave him a smacking
kiss leaving a bright lipstick mark on his cheek.
As he rarely looked in a mirror,
one of his friends tactfully pointed it out.

'Ah, it's just a sacramental emblem,'
he replied with a twinkle.
'The outward and visible sign
of an inward and spiritual whoopee.'

3

UNDERSTANDING

One of the brothers broke the handle off a cup,
and was just about to drop it in the waste bin
when St Lynas stopped him.

'Don't do that! Think of the spastics and disabled!'
'Why?' said the lad, 'they don't want cups without handles!'
'Maybe not. But they're God's breakages, and he never
throws them away,
but uses them for something else.'

And taking the cup
he carried it carefully out to the greenhouse.

4

SYMPATHY

The brothers were tut-tutting and chuntering one night
over the latest idiocies of people in the newspaper.

'Don't be too critical,' said St Lynas,
'it all depends on your point of view.'
'There were once two flies on the ceiling,
and one said to the other-
'It's crazy, they spend all that money
on this beautiful ceiling and what do they do?
Walk on the floor!'

5
MAKING DO

St Lynas wanted to replace a pane of clear glass in the shed window, so he went to the glazier's and asked for a piece 18 inches wide by 24 inches high.

The glazier, who was an old friend, said with a twinkle in his eye,
'I'm terribly sorry but I've only got a piece 24 inches wide by 18 inches high.'

'Oh dear,' said St Lynas in mock sorrow.
'Never mind, I'll put it in sideways:
the chances are no-one will notice!'
And looking at his friend he said,
'A good man is a good man—standing up or lying down!'

6

HUMANITY

St Lynas was going into the little chapel one morning for prayers
when he stubbed his toe on the step.
Hopping around in agony he eventually said
with great vehemence 'Aswan!!'

'Why "Aswan"?' said one brother to another.
'Well, it's the biggest one he could think of,'
was the reply.

7

BEING RUDE TO GOD

'What's blasphemy?' they asked St Lynas,
after reading in the paper about some trouble in another country.

'It's being rude to God,' said St Lynas, looking up from his book.
'Is it possible to be rude to God?' they persisted.
'No,' grunted St Lynas.
'Then what's blasphemy?'

Laying aside his book with a sigh, he good-humouredly explained.
'Blasphemy is being rude about a God who doesn't exist—
it's only a crime according to people who don't know him very well,
and think he needs protecting.'

8

WONDER

St Lynas' disciples kept shooing one of his cats away
from the chapel where he was saying his prayers.
But he stopped them because their noise was worse
than putting up with the cat.
The animal curled up in front of the altar in a patch of sunlight,
whereupon St Lynas spent a couple of hours ignoring his
prayer book
and just looking at the cat.
Coming out of the chapel they asked what was so fascinating
about it.

'Haven't you ever been amazed,' he said,
'that the Creator put holes in its fur just where its eyes are?'

9

DEATH

The conversation turned to the subject of death one
lunchtime, and they asked St Lynas whether he was
afraid of dying.

'Imagine a guest at a party,' he replied.
'He has met some interesting people,
given good advice to some,
and accepted good advice from others.
He's enjoyed the conversation,
eaten and drunk enough nice things to make him pleasantly
full,
and now he's rather tired and would like to go home.
Would he be afraid to go?'

REJOICING IN THE WRONG

Standing with St Lynas in the newsagents, the village atheist
bought a local newspaper and said,
'I don't know why I buy this rag,
everybody in the village knows what everybody else is doing
anyway!'

'Ah, I know why,' replied St Lynas. 'And it doesn't do you
much credit—
you want to find out who's been caught doing it!'

11

SACRAMENT

Coming out of church one Sunday, where worship included
Holy Communion, St Lynas felt uplifted.

'I feel helped,' he said to his companions,
'both by the sermon and the sacrament.
One idea occurred to me, though.'

'What's that?' they asked.

'Well, in the sermon I was looking at a print—
in the sacrament I was looking at a transparency.'

12

GOD'S UNTIDINESS

One of St Lynas' favourite prayers was
'From the tidy minds of all bureaucrats, Good Lord deliver us.'

One day a visiting civil servant took objection to this
and challenged him about it.

'Think of a child running through an old meadow,
thanking God for cornflowers, buttercups, poppies,' said St
Lynas.
'That's me.'

'Now think of a farmer going through the same meadow,
bewailing all the weeds that have invaded the cows' grass.
That's you!'

13
JOY IN CREATION

St Lynas had two cats, Edie (short for Edipuss)
and Maggie (short for Magnificat).
One windy day, they had a fit of kittenish behaviour,
chasing each other, and their own tails.

St Lynas watched them with a smile, and then sighed and said,
'Well, I'd better get on . . .'
'Why?' asked God, 'it'd do you good to play.'
St Lynas wasn't convinced.

'Look Lynas,' emphasised God. 'If I can spend my day off
teaching kittens to chase their tails, the least you can do
is sit and be amused by it!'

14
THE SOUND OF GOD

An acoustic engineer was visiting St Lynas.
'Do you know,' he said 'in our factory there's a room
so insulated against sound that it is perfectly silent?'
'Can you hear anything at all?' asked St Lynas.
'Just your own heartbeat and breathing,' was the reply.
'Just yourself?' asked St Lynas, appalled.
'Yes.'

After thinking for a while St Lynas said,
'I think I'd rather be with other people—
where I can hear God.'

SEEING GOD

St Lynas and the village atheist were sitting in the shade of the Buttercross, companionably eating ice cream on a very hot day.
But the atheist couldn't let St Lynas go without getting a point in.
'I've kept asking, but no-one can ever tell me what God looks like.'

'Oh I know,' replied St Lynas. 'He looks like electricity.'
'And I also know what Jesus looks like,' he continued.

'Really?' said the atheist.
'Yep!' replied St Lynas.
'To me he looks like you, and to you he looks like me.'

GOD'S LOVE

On a rainy day St Lynas happened to see a worm
in the cobbled yard, slithering down a drain.
He stopped and tried to pick it up on the ferrule of his
umbrella, and put it on the garden. But it kept slithering off.
St Lynas gave up and walked on, but then stopped, turned,
went back, and picked up the worm with his fingers,
and put it on the earth in the flower border.

Looking up to the sky he said,
'Lord, I know it's tempting,
but put your umbrella away—
pick me up with your fingers please!'

DEPRESSION

One day a mournful visitor came to see St Lynas
and spent the whole morning pouring out his woes.
Every one of the clouds in his sky had a pitch black lining.

When he could get a word in, St Lynas asked:
'Have you read the Isaiah bit about "The Man of Sorrows
who was acquainted with grief"?'
'My constant reading!' the man replied.
'Then go home, read it again, and think hard about the word
"ACQUAINTED".'

MIRACLE

St Lynas and two friends were leaning over a five-bar gate
looking at a glorious sunset.
'What a great paintbox God had!' exclaimed one of them.
'Nonsense,' said the other,
'it's just dust in the atmosphere changing the wave patterns
of the light.'

'You're both wrong,' said St Lynas.
'The miracle is this side of the gate.
It's *we* who are moved and call it beautiful.'

PRINCIPLES

As St Lynas was going down the road one day
he came across a man badly treating his dog.
Although the mildest of men, St Lynas roundly cursed the man
and threatened to beat him up.
This shocked the brothers who were with him.

'We've never heard you swear like that,' they said,
'and you're a peaceable fellow on principle!'
'Maybe,' he replied, 'but I'm a Christian first—
principles are what people have instead of God.'

SEEING OURSELVES

'It's good to know ourselves, isn't it?' asked a pensive
brother one day.
'Yes,' said St Lynas. 'We can't love ourselves properly unless
we do.'

'Well, how is it that I can't see myself as I really am?'

'Knowing ourselves like that can only be done by God',
replied St Lynas. 'You can't see yourself as you really are,
because you've got in the way.'

IMPOSSIBILITIES

St Lynas spent some time in the field
looking at a caterpillar on a leaf.
When the brothers asked him what he was looking at he
replied:

'I'm just waiting for a butterfly to go overhead,
so that I can catch the caterpillar looking up at it.
I bet it says "You wouldn't catch me going up in one of
those things!"'

HOLY IDIOTS

'People say we are foolish to live here like this,'
said one of the brothers after coming back from the village,
'being sacrificial, caring for people, and praying.'

'Yet,' said another brother, 'we reckon that people who don't
have any time for faith are living in a fool's paradise, don't
we?'

'So it boils down to the fact that we have to be one sort of
fool or another,' said St Lynas, 'blessed fools, or damned
fools!'

And he stumped out to the garden.

LOVE OF GOD

St Lynas always had a healthy disrespect for ecclesiastical
authority.
'When I look at these stuffed shirts,
I always think "one day not so long ago a woman
took you on her lap and dusted your bottom with talcum
powder!"'

The brothers were a little shocked at this, and said
'But surely you must acknowledge their wisdom!'

'Wisdom, maybe,' replied St Lynas, 'but I'm not so sure that
they know any more about the love of God now,
than they did when they were squalling babies!'

24

REWARDS

After an uproarious Sunday evening supper, when two
welcome guests had been the life and soul of the party,
and the house was full of good fellowship, St Lynas sighed
and said:

'When a family has a Sunday like this—
full of happiness and grace,
a good angel knocks on the door and says
"may all your Sundays be like this".

But when a family has a Sunday full of regret,
bitterness or selfishness,
a bad angel knocks on the door and says
"may all your Sundays be like this."'

25

NOTICING

Walking through the fields one day,
the brothers were talking about the difference
between seeing and noticing.

Taking a conker from underneath a great horse chestnut tree,
St Lynas said to one of them,
'Break it open.' He did.
'What do you see inside it?' asked St Lynas.
'Nothing much, just pap,' said the brother.

Looking closely at it with some care, St Lynas said:
'Ah, but I see another great horse chestnut tree.'

26

WATER INTO WINE

St Lynas had been reading the story of the miracle at the
marriage feast at Cana.

'Lord,' he pondered, 'when it comes to me
you've some pretty grubby water to start with.'

'Granted,' replied God, 'champagne it won't be.

But with a bit of effort by both of us I reckon I can turn you
into a reasonably acceptable plonk.'

27

WORDS

St Lynas and the brothers went to the big church in
the town to hear the famous theologian preach.
It was a very impressive sermon,
filled with wide perspectives and technical terms.

'What did you think of it?' they asked him
as they travelled back on the bus.

'He didn't use many long words.'
'But the sermon was full of them!' they said.
'No, I meant REALLY long words,' replied St Lynas.
'Words like "God" and "Love", or "Joy" and "Peace".'

28

SYNCOPATION

Giving a penniless wanderer a sandwich in the kitchen one day, St Lynas listened to his tales of woe.

'I think I know the heart of your difficulty my friend,' he said. 'You're suffering from syncopation.'

'Syncopation?'

'Yes,' explained St Lynas. 'Irregular movement from bar to bar!'

29

PRAYER

The village atheist tackled St Lynas in the market one Saturday.

'Hey,' he said, 'you're good at prayers. I've put £10 on a horse in the three thirty, I want you to pray for him to win. If you do, and it does, I'll go to church tomorrow.'

'You're like the man who took his canary to the chiropodist to make it chirrup,'
replied St Lynas.
'I'm very much afraid you've come to the wrong shop!'

MATERIALISM

St Lynas and a businessman were sprawled in deckchairs
one sunny afternoon.
The businessman was running through the plans he had
for increasing his turnover.

'By all means grasp your opportunities,' said St Lynas,
'but always hold them at arm's length.'

'What do you mean by that?' the man asked.

'Take a five pound note, and hold it at arm's length,' said
St Lynas,
'and it'll be just one part of what you see.
Put it over your eyes, and it will blot out the heavens!'

ACTIVITY

People sometimes nagged St Lynas for doing too much,
for although he took things at a steady pace,
after he'd fed the birds he was always occupied.

To one of them he said:
'There was once a man who wanted to live to be a hundred,
so he studied all the latest ideas for living longer.
Then he shut himself into a room, away from sight and
sound of other people;
he sat in a meditative posture, and wrapped himself in
tranquil thoughts.'

'And is he still alive?' the visitor asked.
'No,' said St Lynas. 'He died the day he went in there.'

COMMERCIALISM

The village atheist was in the newsagents paying for his
papers, when he noticed St Lynas sorting through the
stationery shelves, and muttering to himself.

'What's up, Lynas?' he asked.

'Typical of modern life!' complained St Lynas.
'All I want is a plain book to write things in—and what do
I find?
Every single one of them is ruled for pounds and pence!'

THE KNOW-ALL

If there was one sort of visitor who irritated St Lynas
it was the bigoted 'know-all'.
After one such guest had departed,
having made everyone feel small with his name-dropping,
St Lynas quietly asked:

'How did he sign his name in the visitors' book?'
'Just normally,' the brothers replied.

'Oh,' said St Lynas, disappointed.
'He struck me as the sort who would sign with three x's,
one for his title, one for his name, and one for his Ph.D.'

34

NEARNESS

Working in the cabbage patch one day
St Lynas was very aware of God.
'Lord, you always speak to me in English.
Do you speak every language in the world
in order to talk to everyone?'

'No,' said God. 'I'm not much of a linguist at all, truth be
told—at least not in any language men would understand.'

'Then how come you talk to me?' said St Lynas.
'I don't,' said God, 'I only *think*—you're the one who does
all the talking.'

'Touché!' said St Lynas, and got on with the cabbages
in complete but comfortable silence.

CONTENTMENT

One day St Lynas accompanied his colleagues to the local
town for a rare visit.
They all 'ooh'd' and 'aah'd' over the latest fashions
and electronic marvels in the shops—none of which they
could afford.
Walking back they were all quietly thoughtful, except St
Lynas, who was whistling merrily.

'What makes you so cheerful?' they asked.
'I'm just so happy,' he replied,
'that I haven't seen anything today that I wanted.'

CHURCH

St Lynas was walking home from church one Sunday morning,
and the brothers were discussing what a variety of people
there were in the congregation.
His contribution to the conversation was:

'Some Christians are like wheelbarrows—they need to be
pushed.
Some are like kites—they fly away unless a string is put on them.
Some are like balloons—full of air and ready to explode.
Some are like rugby balls—you can't tell which way they'll
bounce next.'

'And which are you?' they asked him.
'What I'm *trying* to be,' he said,
'is one of God's door handles!'

37

FINDING GOD

'Where is God?' St Lynas' disciples once asked him.

In reply he told them about two very stupid peasants,
one of whom tried to run away from his footprints,
and the other tried to run away from his shadow.

'Then the only way to escape was to stand still in the shade,'
they suggested.

'Oh no,' said St Lynas.
'Even then they'd be standing in them and surrounded by them.
There is NO escape from God.'

PERSONHOOD

'There are many kinds of people,' said St Lynas one day.

'Wise people who know others;
Honest people who know themselves;
Strong people who master others;
And truly powerful people who master themselves.'

'Which are you?' asked the brothers.
'I'm just a person who looks at the other people, and prays,'
he replied.

39

GOD'S SYSTEM

As St Lynas' dead friend left no will,
he was asked to divide his estate among the four children.

'By man's laws, or God's?' he asked.
'By God's method,' the children replied.

So looking at the four of them he awarded one £5, another
£50,000, another the car, and another an old mattress.

They vigorously protested, 'Is this the law of God?'
'Just look around you,' said St Lynas, 'see the different ways
God distributes his talents'.

So, as they should, they took the decision to the Probate
Office
which works by man's laws.

40

FISHING

The curate from the local church came to lunch one day,
and was telling St Lynas that his church seemed to be filled
with awkward, emotionally inadequate, and difficult people.

'And you're surprised?' asked St Lynas.
'My dear fellow, any fisherman knows that when he casts
the hook,
the awkward ones get caught first, the smoothies escape.'

'But keep at it—you'll get them all in the end!'

41

RULES

If there was one subject which brought St Lynas out in
purple rage it was the planning department.

One breakfast he had read a letter from them turning down
his idea to extend the barn to make visitors' bedrooms.

'Lord, I can understand why you made idiots,'
he said, looking at the ceiling with sorrow,
'that was just for practice. But why then did you go on to
perfect the model with town and country planners?'

THE UNDESERVING

The brothers were always complaining that St Lynas was a 'soft touch', and that he gave away too much to people who didn't deserve help.

'My dears,' he said. 'Everybody helps the "deserving poor", it's our job to help the "undeserving poor".'

And he pointed to the man the Good Samaritan helped. 'That bird-brain travelled the dangerous road from Jerusalem to Jericho by himself!' he said.
'If ever there was a case of a fellow deserving everything he got—it was him!
But still he got helped.'

'I'm just "doing likewise."'

43

MIRACULOUS FAITH

St Lynas joined the village atheist on the street corner where he was looking disconsolately at the front end of his car, which was stove in.

'Just my luck! I need it tonight,' said the atheist.
'Now if God would do a miracle, and mend it in front of me, I'd probably believe in him.'

'No you wouldn't,' said St Lynas, 'because you've got it the wrong way round.
Miracles never cause faith, they're always the result of faith.'

'But if it's any help, I'll do you a little miracle and lend you our minibus.'

44

HYPOCRISY

Talking about hypocrisy one day, St Lynas told the brothers
of one man
who saw a 'Wayside Pulpit' which read:
'This Church is full of sinners, come in and make one more.'
So he did.

'But he didn't stay long—he couldn't stand the way that the
people didn't live up to the standards of Christ,' continued
St Lynas.

'He needed them to lie—to pretend to be saints,' he said.

'And did they?' they asked him.
'No, thank God!' replied St Lynas.
'So he went to another church where they did.'

45

FASTING

St Lynas' friends were bothered by the fact that he didn't
observe the usual fast days.
'The important fast is the fast of the heart,' he replied.
'You must cease listening with your ears
and listen with your heart.
It is for ears to hear and the mind to cogitate,
but the heart should be empty, restful,
and waiting to be filled.'

46

SUFFERING

The most common problem St Lynas is consulted about is
suffering.
'I don't know the answer,' he usually says,
'I haven't got a hard heart or a soft head!

But he often says that suffering can be like a bit of sand
that gets inside an oyster—uncomfortable and painful,
—the only way it can be tolerated is by coating it with a
special deposit,
which the oyster does.

'Most oysters keep out of trouble, and live normal natural
lives,' he emphasises.
'It's the ones which suffer that produce the pearls.'

GRATITUDE

St Lynas caught a 'stomach bug' and had alternated between
the loo and bed for two days.

The third day he was better and looked with joy out of his
bedroom window at a gorgeous morning.

'Thanks, Lord, for the beautiful blue sky,
but most of all for getting my innards working properly.'

'I appreciate your priorities,' said God warmly.
'The sky was simple—just a long handled roller,
but your plumbing gave me the dickens of a job
before I got it right.'

48

HANDS

One of the brothers cut his hand while mending the fence
of the old lady who lived up the road.

As he was cleaning the dirt off his hand, and bandaging it,
St Lynas said:

'Hands are interesting, aren't they?'
'In what way?' asked the brother.

'Well, which are more beautiful?' posed St Lynas.
'The hands of a manicurist from the Beauty Parlour,
the hands of a young lady model from a magazine,
or the dirty and cracked hands of a mother who has
just scrubbed the floor for her children to play on?'

49

GIVING

St Lynas was told a sob story by a wandering tramp, who talked him out of £20.

When he got to the gate with the money he turned and yelled, 'It's all lies!'
St Lynas yelled back, 'Promise you won't tell anyone else at all'.
'Why?' asked the tramp.
'Because if you do, you'll stop people giving to those who are genuinely in need.
You will be the cause of many needy people not being helped.'

The tramp thought, tucked the £20 in the gate-post, and walked away.
But he now pops in regularly for a cup of tea.

50

HONESTY

St Lynas was carrying a basket of eggs to sell at the village market when a couple of chasing dogs knocked him over, smashing the eggs on the road.

The stall holders, who had a soft spot for him, rallied round with a collection to pay for the eggs.

'That's so kind of you,' said St Lynas, pulling a piece of paper out of the smashed eggs on the tarmac, and wiping it. 'Let's see—the eggs would have raised £15, you've given me £20.65p. What about putting the difference into the Oxfam box at the chemists?'

'Brilliant,' said the man operating the tea bar.
'Have a drink on me!'

51

PURPOSE

A businessman once spent a week 'recharging his batteries'
with the community.
Sitting in the barn with St Lynas one day he said:
'I don't seem to have any purpose in life, any usefulness.'

'I'm sure you have,' said St Lynas, 'but if you want a simple
rule, almost childish, try this.
Every day do something good for someone else,
only regard the days when you don't as wasted days.
That's 365 good deeds a year. In 40 years that comes to
14,600 people's lives you've made a bit happier.'

And St Lynas smiled, 'even you can't sneeze at that!'

52

ATTITUDE

A new recruit to the group came with starry expectations
that everything was going to be easy. But living in
community never is.
Talking to him, St Lynas said:

'The secret is thankfulness, thankfulness in everything,'
he said. 'Don't curse because the roses have thorns on
them—be thankful that the thorns have roses.'

SAMARITAN WHO?

St Lynas was walking back from the village one day
when he came across a lady driver whose car had stopped.
She reckoned the dipstick for the oil was too short.

St Lynas fetched the minibus and towed her to the nearest
garage.
She offered him some money, but he naturally refused it.

'At least tell me your name,' she asked.
'On one condition,' said St Lynas.
'That you tell me the name of the Good Samaritan—God be
with you!'

As St Lynas laughingly said to the brothers at supper,
'She'll be reading her Bible more tonight than she's done
for years!'

54
THE DARK NIGHT

St Lynas, usually a sunny character, has his times of
depression.
During one such time he had this imaginary discussion.

'God, if you're there, I think I'm spiritually dried-up, dead!'
'Well, we can soon see,' whispered God. 'Have you wept at
anything recently?'
'Yes,' said Lynas, remembering a gravely sick child.
'Has your heart beaten faster at something beautiful?'
'Yes,' said Lynas, thinking of the morning fields.
'Have you really *listened* when people talked to you?'
'Yes—sometimes,' said Lynas, trying to be honest.

'Then you may be an awkward old cuss,' said God,
'but you're certainly not dead!'

55
ECCENTRICITY

An engineer friend of St Lynas had spent a week with them,
and told them after supper one night, 'You're a lot of raving
eccentrics!'

'In what way?' bristled St Lynas.

'Well, the definition of an eccentric is something which has
a centre outside its own, if you want the technicalities,'
replied the engineer.

'Ah well,' said St Lynas with a beaming smile, 'I plead guilty
to *that*.
Because it means that every Christian has a positive *duty*
to be eccentric!'

MEMORIES

Two of the younger brothers were behind the greenhouse
one day plotting
how to play a trick on one of the others.
Though he was unseen, St Lynas overheard the
conversation.

Sticking his head round the corner like a gargoyle, he said:
'How do you reckon your plan rates as a good leg-pull?'

'Quite ingenious,' they replied.
'And how do you reckon it rates as a memory in the years
ahead?'
St Lynas added.

'In all honesty, not so good,' they replied.
'Then as you've got to live with your memories,'
he said kindly, 'best leave it at the idea stage, eh?'

57
DECORATING

When St Lynas and two of his early friends first came across
the almost derelict farm which is now the community,
they were appalled at the condition of the house.

'It'll take a heck of a lot of redecorating!' said one of the
brothers, looking at the faded paper and peeling paint.

'Absolutely!' said St Lynas, sitting on a windowsill, and
looking serious.
'A lot of redecorating . . .', but clearly he saw the problem
differently.

'Someone who lived here was very unhappy.
So it will need a thorough clean-out, a priming of prayer,
several solid coats of love, and a nice bright topcoat of
laughter.'

FORGIVENESS

One of the brothers had an upset conscience.
'I've done something terrible, I can't forgive myself!' he said.
'Ah, but you must,' said St Lynas. And he told this story.

'An old legend says that everyone has two angels.
One sits on our right shoulder and when we do anything
good, he writes it down in a big book.

On our left shoulder sits another who writes down anything
we do wrong, but in pencil.
If, before we go to bed, we bow our heads and say
"Gracious Father, I've sinned, forgive me," then he rubs the
entry out.
If we don't, he inks it in.'

GOD KNOWS

St Lynas never reacts much when good or bad things
happen.
He tends to say, 'Good? Bad? God knows!'

He once told the tale of a man who travelled on a dangerous
journey with a lamp, a donkey and a rooster.
First, in a gust of wind, the lamp went out.
Then the donkey fell over a cliff,
and the rooster was taken by a wild animal.

As he was resting one night in a wood, he heard an army
pass.

'If the donkey had brayed, the rooster crowed, or they'd
seen the lamp,
he would have been killed,' said St Lynas.
'So whether anything is good or bad—only God knows!'

60

WISDOM

Much of the brothers' time was taken up with learning.
They each had a course of study to follow,
and consulted St Lynas whenever they felt like it.

He has a standard talk which he gives to new arrivals.
'You will learn here the art of ignorance, coupled with the
grace of humility.
You will begin by thinking that you need to know everything.
After a year or two you will think you *do* know everything.
Then you will gradually discover that you know much less.

And when you get to saying "I don't know" often and happily,
—you've graduated!'

CO-OPERATION

One week the community had a continual stream of people coming for hand-outs of food or money.

'Why is it,' the brothers asked St Lynas, 'that when God made so many poor people, he didn't fix up some way of feeding them?'

'He did—and we're it!' St Lynas replied.
'When God made the world he left the rivers unbridged, the poetry unwritten, the songs unsung,
the stories untold, and the food undistributed.'

'God isn't such a fool as to fill the world with unemployed layabouts!'

62

CREATION

'Lord,' asked St Lynas one day, 'why did you create people when you must have known the evil they would do?'

'My dear Lynas,' replied God, asking a question he already knew the answer to.
'Have you had children?'
'Yes', said St Lynas, 'long ago.'

'And what did you do when they were born?' asked God.
'We celebrated the joy of it all,' replied St Lynas.
'But didn't you know that they would suffer and die?'
'We didn't think of that in our happiness.'

'Exactly,' said God.

63
BREAKFAST

There was a big argument over breakfast as to what was the best start to the day.

'Ah,' said St Lynas, while pouring a cup of coffee.
'I remember a Methodist preacher at an inter-church conference praying
"Lord, may we not be like porridge, stiff, stodgy and hard to stir,
but like cornflakes, fresh and ready to serve."'

'But then,' St Lynas said between sips, 'the Church of Scotland minister prayed
"Lord grant that we shall not be like cornflakes, lightweight, brittle and cold,
but like porridge—warm, comforting and full of goodness."'

Smiling sweetly, he added, 'pass the toast and marmalade please!'

MEDITATION

One of the brothers went to St Lynas and complained that
another of the brothers
spent too much time sitting and thinking.
'Leave him be,' said St Lynas, 'if he's thinking, he's all right.'

'It reminds me of the letter which an orchestra conductor
received,' he continued.
'It read: "As someone who paid for a front row ticket, I think
it only fair to tell you that the men who scraped the big
fiddle things did nothing most of the time,
and only played when you were looking at them."'

SICK VISITING

'It's just down the side road, the third cottage on the left,
number 23,'
said St Lynas, giving directions to one of the brothers who
was sick visiting.

'And when you get there, press the bell push twice with
your elbow,'
he continued.

'Twice?' asked the brother.

'Then she'll know it's us.'

'And why press with my elbow?'

'Well,' replied St Lynas, 'you're not going empty-handed,
are you?'

SELF-PORTRAIT

'What's that supposed to be?' asked one brother,
looking at a painting in the Town Art Gallery.
'Is it the right way up?' said another,
as they wandered to look at the more traditional paintings.

St Lynas pondered that far from showing life,
each artist was really painting his attitude to life.
'Every artist is in fact,' he said, 'doing an autobiography.'

'So are we all come to think of it,' he continued,
'in actions, and speech, and attitudes.'

A brother picked up the thought, 'Whether it's a Sistine
Chapel ceiling
or an unintelligible daub.'

'Quite,' said St Lynas.

CONFUSED

The brothers had been taken by St Lynas to hear a lecture
on modern theological trends with the emphasis on Process
Theology.

Having a quiet word with God that night, St Lynas said:
'Lord, I know I wasn't at the front of the queue when you
issued intelligence,
but I honestly don't grasp what he was getting at.'

'Me neither,' said God.
'He certainly went a long way round to get to the point.'

'Reminds me,' mused God, 'of the fellow who described a
circle
as a round straight line with a hole in the middle.'

68

WIVES

One day, shopping in the village, St Lynas got involved in an argument with the village atheist.

'Your God's a thief!' he said, with the glint of the perfect argument in his eye.

'Really?' said St Lynas.

'Yes,' came the punchline, 'he stole a rib from Adam.'

'Hmmm,' replied St Lynas, 'suppose someone broke into your house at night,
stole £20, and left £50 in its place.'

'I should be so lucky!' said the atheist.

'But you have been,' said St Lynas.

'You may be down one rib, but you're up by one wife!'

69

PROVIDENCE

The village atheist was reading the paper on the street corner
one market day
when St Lynas passed him with a pleasant 'Good Morning'.
'Look at all this news,' said the atheist. 'Where's your God
in all this war, crime and disaster?'

'I saw him on the way into the village,' answered St Lynas.
'Every one of the newborn lambs in the fields had a mother
to look after it.'

70

GROWING

One of the young men wandering around with St Lynas
feeding the chickens confided that he didn't feel he was
progressing in the way that the others were.

'I can see them maturing and getting spiritually deeper,
but as for me, I'm stuck!' he said.

'I've got two points to make about that,' replied St Lynas.
'First, everyone gets stuck sometimes, like a daffodil when
the flowers have finished, and that's the time for building
up strength.'

'The second thing is not to measure yourself against others—
take things at your own pace.
Observe the snail who, with a sigh,
said "see those turtles whizzing by."'

MODERN WORSHIP

Sitting in the village tea shop with the local vicar,
St Lynas was regaled with all his new plans for experimental
worship at the church.

'Hmmm,' replied St Lynas when he could get a word in.
'But will your people get spiritual backache?'

'What do you mean?' asked the vicar.

'I once knew a businessman who had his office refurnished
with the most modern and stylish equipment,
but suffered from terrible backache as a result.
When he called in the furnishers to check everything,
they found he'd spent two weeks sitting in the waste paper
bin.'

HABIT

Olive came in once a week from the village to do the
community letters.

After one heavy day's dictation St Lynas told her with a smile,
'And when you finish off your prayers tonight, my dear,
they should end with "Amen" not "Yours sincerely."'

73

INCARNATION

One summer day St Lynas had been in the chapel praying,
which he had found calming and helpful.
But when he came outside God said, 'Good morning, Lynas'.

'My, you made me jump, Lord!' said St Lynas.
'Why weren't you in there with me?'
'Well, I am quite often,' said God, 'but I spend most of my
time out here.'

'Ah!' said St Lynas,
'you mean that you speak to me mostly through ordinary
people, and routine things!'
'You've got it,' said God, 'and by the way . . .'

'Yes?' asked St Lynas, in the bright June sunshine.

'Happy Christmas!' said God.

74

THANKFULNESS

Kind people often sent gifts to the community. One lady sent pies which were, to be honest, inedible, and had to be thrown in the dust bin.

St Lynas, however, always thanked her politely by saying: 'Thank you so much for another pie, they never last long here!'

Another sent books which no-one wanted. He was told that 'St Lynas would lose no time in reading them.'

75

MYSTERY

The village atheist said one day, 'How can I follow a God I can't understand?'
'Just by admitting he *is*,' said St Lynas.

'You just go and stand in the middle of the busy street, and when the ambulance comes to fetch you, refuse to go until they make you understand how the differential gear works.'

'But that's crazy,' said the atheist.

'Of course,' replied St Lynas.

PRAISE

Someone who was staying for a week noticed that one of
St Lynas' chores was to boil the eggs for breakfast.
As he did it, he would sing, and as it was before breakfast,
enthusiastically but not too tunefully.

Always it was the same hymn 'O For a Thousand Tongues
to Sing.'
'I quite like that hymn,' said the visitor,
'but can't he sing a different one, just for a change?'

'Oh no,' said one of the brothers, 'that would ruin the system.
It's six verses for soft, and eight for hard.'

77

NEIGHBOURLINESS

St Lynas tried to have a day off every week, even though it tended to move about because of the demands on his time. The friends, however, tried to honour his rest and relieved him of his chores for the day.

But he didn't help things by hanging a notice on the door which said:

Day off. Do not disturb unless you want to see me.

78

FAULTS

The village atheist was in an unusually chatty mood when he joined St Lynas at the café table on market day.

'Why is it that people have so many faults?' he asked. 'I've been let down this week time after time.'

'I've often wondered about that,' said St Lynas. 'I reckon that it's all to do with the order of creation.'

'In what way?'

'Well,' St Lynas went on, 'think of it, if God had all that work to do, he'd be pretty tired by the time he made us on the Friday.'

79

SIGNPOSTS

Walking back from the village one day, St Lynas and the brothers were discussing the role of the Bible for the Christian.

As they came to a signpost at a crossroads, St Lynas wrapped himself round it, and held on tight.

'What on earth are you doing?' they asked him.
'I'm pretending to be someone who only sees the *words* of the Bible,' he said.

'Don't be so silly—we'll be late for lunch,' they protested.
'Precisely,' said St Lynas. 'And very biblical, too!'

80

RESURRECTION

'Why so sad, Lynas?' asked God quietly,
as St Lynas was returning from the local airport
where he had said 'goodbye' to an old friend whom he might not see again.

'I was just wondering why life is so full of little deaths,'
said St Lynas,
'partings, changes in jobs, the end of friendships,
each one a small bereavement.'

'Ah,' said God, 'it's just my way of giving you a bit of practice.
If you can find a resurrection after the little deaths,
then you'll have no problem with the big one.'

CHRISTIANS

In the village market one day the village atheist told St Lynas
he was thinking of emigrating.

'But I don't know where to go,' he said.
'America is too full of Christians for my taste,
while Africa and the Far East are getting fuller of them by
the day.
Finland might be an idea. Very few Finnish people go to
church.'

'Why not go to hell?' said St Lynas, adjusting his rucksack.
'There aren't any real Christians there at all!'

GOING BACK

St Lynas was depressed. Somehow God seemed far away.
So he decided to have a day's ramble back to the little
country chapel where God first became real to him. Perhaps
he would become real again.

Packing sandwiches, he found the chapel
and knelt in the quietness.
'Are you there God?' he asked.
'Of course,' said God. 'I'm here in your rucksack.
What did you bring me all the way back here for?'

83
EVANGELISM

An itinerant evangelist called at the community one day.
'How many people have you converted?' he asked St Lynas.

'Ah, that's easy!' said St Lynas, 'none.'
'God has converted a few while I've been here,
but it's all a bit of a mystery to me,' he continued.

'You see, what I say can help people who know what I mean,
and who don't really need it,
but doesn't mean a thing to those without faith who need it.'

'So you don't do any good?' replied the evangelist.
'Probably not,' said St Lynas. 'God does, though.'

84
LOOKING FOR GOD

Sitting in the market café one day,
the local atheist told St Lynas, 'I've searched for God
everywhere, and I can't find him. Where is he?'

'I'll answer that in a moment, as soon as I can find my
glasses,' said St Lynas.

And slowly he examined every pocket, and went through
his rucksack which he used to carry shopping, without
success.
'You're a silly old man,' said the atheist,
'you've got them on your nose all the time!
You were using them to search for them!'

'So I was!' replied St Lynas, 'how stupid!
Now what were you saying about looking for God?'

THE BUDGET

After listening to the Chancellor's Budget on the radio,
the brothers agreed at tea that none of it had any relevance
to them.

'But wouldn't it be a good idea,' suggested St Lynas,
'if every year the Archbishop of Canterbury announced a
spiritual budget?'

'The balance sheet of the country's morals would be quite
something!'
suggested one brother.

'And some great political schemes would be declared
spiritually bankrupt,'
added St Lynas.

AMERICAN TEA

St Lynas was invited to spend a week in a church in
America.
He had a wonderful time, and admired most of what he saw.
But there was one thing he couldn't take.

He refused to believe that the cold pale brown liquid they
gave him was tea.

So in between sermons he taught them how to make it
properly—warming the pot and using boiling water.

'After all,' he muttered under his breath, 'any civilisation
that can throw two perfectly good shiploads of tea
into a harbour isn't to be trusted with it!'

THUNDEROUS SERMONS

While St Lynas was preaching a sermon in Kansas one
evening there was a tornado warning.

Lightning flashed, thunderous rain came down,
all the lights in the church went out, and the microphone
died.
After 30 seconds everything came back on.

Though this happened three times in the sermon,
St Lynas doggedly carried on throughout.

As the congregation left, one man said to him at the door
'That was great, what are you going to do tomorrow night?'

88

CONFUSION

St Lynas went to look at dinosaur tracks that had been
exposed by the erosion of ancient rocks.
He noticed that in one place the toe marks of two footprints
inches apart were pointing in opposite directions.

'God!' he said, 'I never realised that before.'

'Realised what?' asked God.

'Well, we talk about the "human condition",' explained
St Lynas, 'but I didn't realise you put it in the dinosaurs too.'

'Look at those footprints—
they didn't know whether they were coming or going either!'

MEETING GOD

St Lynas was listening to a group of Americans discussing their cholesterol readings. They asked him what his was.

'I haven't the foggiest idea!' he replied.

'I've every admiration for your enthusiasm for health,' he continued.

'But it strikes me that for a very churchgoing and God-fearing nation,
Americans are remarkably keen not to meet their Maker any earlier than can be helped!'

THE HAPPY SPIRAL

St Lynas found the generosity of his American hosts quite
overwhelming.
Nothing was too much trouble for them, and they were
lavish in their love and time, as well as money.

'Of course I'm truly grateful,' he said.
'But my gratitude is neither here nor there,
you have been generous because you *are* generous,
and because of your generous acts now
you will *become* even more generous.'

And with a twinkle he said, 'St Peter had better watch out!
With this happy spiral of love and action,
you will unscrew the very hinges on the gates of heaven.'

INTEGRITY

Running his hand over a big blue boulder of plastic in the
Kansas Art Gallery St Lynas said, 'I don't like it. It feels
wrong!'

'Ah,' said his companion whimsically, 'that's because you
haven't been to see the Elgin Plastics.'

'Maybe not,' replied St Lynas, 'But I *have* seen the Venus
de Melamine, as well as "The Last Supper" by Leonardo
de Vinyl, and I *still* don't like them!'

LOVE

A couple who were totally deaf came to St Lynas' services at the church, although they couldn't follow a word of what he said.
But they did teach him the American deaf sign using the thumb, first and last fingers, which means 'I Love You.'

He used that sign to them at the end of each service and they went away happy.

'Think of the advantages,' commented St Lynas to the minister of the church.

'This is what we say on behalf of God to all the hearing people and it takes us 20 minutes.
With this couple it only takes a second to preach the entire Gospel!'

93
THE CROSS

Visiting a Catholic chapel on a crag in Arizona, St Lynas
was thrilled not so much by the spectacular view, but
because the Stations of the Cross around the walls were
constructed of old railway spikes and pieces of railway
track.
'Wonderful!' he said, 'how true!'

'What's so special about that?' asked his companions,
who were startled by his enthusiasm for it.

'Don't you see?' he said with his eyes sparkling.
'Or perhaps you Americans have a different term for it.'

'We call the railway "The Permanent Way".'

94
DEPTH OF FAITH

Peering down into the mile deep Grand Canyon
St Lynas was staggered by the size and age of this natural
wonder.

'I'm worried, Lord,' he said.

'A decade I know about; a century I can imagine;
but a million years is an abstraction;
and as for those rocks at the bottom which are half as old
as time . . .'

'Ah, when logic or imagination runs out you need faith,'
said God.
'Haven't you got any?'

'Yes, just like everyone else,' said St Lynas.

'Then what's the problem?' asked God.

95
GOD'S TIME

At the Petrified Forest, St Lynas sat on one of the fallen trees that had been turned into stone.

He wiped his brow with his handkerchief in the paralysing heat and said:

'Lord, if the book can be believed, it took you 228 million years to impregnate these trees with silica. But do me a favour.'

'What?' asked God.

'I appreciate that you will take your time to fill me fully with your grace, but 228 million years is ridiculous!'

96
HELL

While in Las Vegas St Lynas stepped on the moving pavement which whisked him into Caesar's Palace.
He walked among the acres of one-armed bandits, gambling tables, shops and restaurants, mingling with the crowds who had been lured in by promises of amusement and riches.

Having seen it all with a horrified wonder, he tried to get out, but then realised that there were no signs to indicate the exits.

The only solution was to make for a wall and follow it until he found a door.
Once he ended up in the hotel, another time among the dustbins.

'Well, well,' reflected St Lynas. 'Just like hell!'

APPRECIATION

As he was travelling home on the airplane St Lynas was dozing.

'Lord,' he mused, 'I've met lots of wonderful people, and seen some fantastic things, but do you know the most useful thing I've learned?'

'I give up,' said God, 'you tell me.'

'Well,' said St Lynas, 'I've actually found out how to open those little plastic pots of milk without squirting it all over myself.'

'Marvellous!' replied God. 'You must show me how it's done sometime.'

ADVICE

The first job St Lynas had when he got back was to speak at Founder's Day at the local school. Suffering from jet-lag he was in an astringent mood and said to the top class:

'My advice for you is
don't look, you might see,
don't listen, you might hear,
don't think, you might learn.

Don't make a decision, you might be wrong,
don't walk, you might stumble,
don't run, you might fall,
Above all don't live, you might die!'

Afterwards he said to the Headmaster,
'Knowing how contra-suggestible young people are these days, I might even have done some good!'

99
PRIDE

During Lent the brothers had all given up something.
Chocolate, sugar in their tea, television.

But St Lynas kept quiet during the discussion as to which
deprivation was most pleasing to the Almighty.
At the end of an inconclusive argument
they thought to ask him what he had given up.

His answer was simple—'Self-righteousness.'

100
LOVE THE MOST

Idly chatting to God while pruning the roses one day, St
Lynas said:
'There's one thing, Lord, I've been meaning to ask you for
a long time.'

'Ask away,' said God.

'Which of all your children do you love the best?'
'Ah,' replied God. 'The sick until they get better,
the young until they grow up, and the estranged until they
come home.'

'What about folk like me?' asked St Lynas, feeling left out.
'Well, you're helping me do the loving,' said God,
'aren't you?'

SIMPLICITY

The local policeman, drinking his coffee in the kitchen one day, complained to St Lynas of one lady in the village who was always calling him out in the night, because she was convinced that there was a man hiding under her bed.

'Nothing I can do will convince her that there isn't!' he said. 'Several times a week it happens!'

St Lynas went to see the lady, and cured the problem very simply.
He sawed the legs off the bed.

BIBLE READING

'I've been reading the Bible!' said the village atheist,
outside the post office one morning.
'Congratulations!' said St Lynas.

'But I don't believe the ridiculous story that Jonah was
swallowed by a whale, do you?' asked the atheist.
'Well, when I get to heaven I'll ask him,' St Lynas said
accommodatingly.

'What if he isn't there?' said the atheist.
'In that case,' replied St Lynas, *you'll* have to ask him!'

EMPTINESS

One of the brothers was feeling a bit 'down'.
Sitting at the back of the chapel with him after lunch, St
Lynas said:

'A little emptiness is good for us.
Think of it—a solid cup or jug would be an absurdity.
Equally silly would be a house where all the rooms are solid
brick.
The structure is important, but even more vital are the
spaces—the rooms, the doors, the windows'.

'So the emptiness is important?' asked the brother.
'Yes,' said St Lynas, 'when God made us he left a space
inside us.'

'But what about all those people who say God is filling that
space completely?'
asked the brother.
'Don't believe most of them,' said St Lynas.

104

SELF-SACRIFICE

After watching the Remembrance Day parade at the village
cenotaph, when the old men had walked gently down the
road proudly wearing their medal ribbons, St Lynas
discussed it with his companions.

'I'd never realised it until today,' he said.
'Realised what?' they asked.

'Well, think of those medals,' St Lynas said.
'They stand for courage and self-sacrifice.
Many of them, the best ones, are not called "Medals"
or "Orders", but "Crosses."'

105

PERSEVERANCE

A Trade Union officer was staying with St Lynas for a
weekend, and they discussed his work one evening in the
garden.

'Don't get discouraged!' said St Lynas.

'In 1645 one vote gave Cromwell control of this country.
In 1649 one vote condemned Charles 1st to death.
In 1776 one vote made America speak English instead of
German,
and in 1923 one vote made Hitler leader of the Nazi Party.'

'Eventually your vote will be crucial.'

GOD'S ANSWER

'I've got a problem, God,' said St Lynas
in his prayers in chapel one day.
'Only one?' said God.

'Well, the current one is this business of whether the body
of Jesus is really in the bread and wine,
or whether he's in the whole of our worship,
or just in us.
What's the answer?'

'That's theology,' said God, 'much too complicated for me.
But if you really want a definitive reply,
it's the same as always—"yes".'

TESTING

St Lynas was hanging around outside the local garage
waiting for the community mini-bus to re-appear
after having its MOT examination.
He idly looked at the pad of forms
which indicated all the parts of the vehicle which had to
be in working order before it passed.

The garage man, seeing his interest said,
'even with all this lot, thousands of people are killed on
the roads!'

'True,' replied St Lynas, 'It makes me wonder if we wouldn't
be a lot safer if we left the cars alone, and tested the drivers
every year?'

GARDEN PARABLE

Showing a visitor round the walled garden, St Lynas said, 'Here's an apple tree, it reminds me of Fred, not much to look at, no nice smell, but plenty of workmanlike fruit.'

Passing a rose bush, he said, 'This is Jenny, marvellous colourful personality, but not very practical.'

Then in the vegetable patch, he said 'These parsnips are George. No sparkling personality, and no fruit, but plenty of goodness underneath.'

'It takes all sorts to make a garden,' mused St Lynas, '—and a world!'

WORSHIP

St Lynas went to a special service in the village with his friends.
It was a boisterous one with plenty of choruses, dancing around, and exuberant prayers.

It made St Lynas feel a bit uncomfortable, so as they went home he said.
'Lord, do you like that sort of worship?'

'Yes and no,' replied God.
'What sort of answer is that?'
'Don't be saucy!' said God.
And then relenting he said, 'I don't mind what people do on the outside of worship: whatever switches them on!
I only hear what's on the inside.'

GOD'S GRAMMAR

St Lynas was quietly reading an old theology book
somebody had given him, and was ploughing through
chapters about the nature of God.

The brothers in the room were startled when he suddenly
stood up, and with great force threw the book through the
open window.
'This book should not be laid aside lightly,' he said
vehemently,
'but thrown with great force!

'What's the matter with it?' they asked.
'The fellow's grammar is all wrong!' said St Lynas.
'God is a verb, not a noun.'

CHILDREN

A young mother with two toddlers was spending a week at the house, and it was one of St Lynas' pleasures to help in bathing them at the end of each day.

He always ended as wet as the children, and all of them shrieking with joy.

As the mother was putting them into their pyjamas St Lynas said:
'Isn't it wonderful that God made toddlers not only washable, but also shrink-proof, and crease-resisting!'

RIGHTEOUSNESS

After the school Speech Day, where he had given the
prizes, St Lynas was pondering over the youngsters who
had played their instruments.

'I won't mention names,' said St Lynas,
'but some of them were very righteous.'

'What do you mean—righteous?' the brothers asked him.

'Well, they played every note right, the fingering was right,
the tempo was right, and yet it wasn't music.
They were getting it all wrong!'

'The Christian way is to throw your heart and soul into it,
capture the composer's mood, and hang the accuracy!'

CHARITY

One day a lady came and gave some money to be spent on charity.
St Lynas went to the fridge and pulled out one of a selection of charity boxes.

'Why on earth do you keep them in the fridge?' asked the lady, with her eyes popping.
'They're not likely to go bad are they?'

'Simple,' said St Lynas, explaining what everyone else already knew.
'It reminds me that charity is to my faith what the fridge is to my food—it preserves it.'

PERSECUTION

The village atheist rushed in and sat with St Lynas in the café, with his back to the door, because he was trying to avoid a widow who wouldn't let him alone.

'I can't understand why she keeps chasing me!' he complained.
'Ah, that's because you look like her third husband,' said St Lynas.
'Third? She's only been married twice,' said the atheist.
'Exactly!' said St Lynas.

THINKING POSITIVELY

A man complained to St Lynas that he had spent all the weekend making a new cement path to his front door, and when he got up on Monday, he found that a dog had walked all the way up it before it had set, leaving a trail of indelible prints.

'What do I do now?' he asked St Lynas in despair.

'Remember,' replied St Lynas, 'it isn't what happens that is important, it's making the best of it.'

'Just rename the house ***Paws Here***,
and everyone will say "How clever!"'

GUILT

Waiting at a bus stop, St Lynas was tackled by a fellow
passenger who said, 'I never go to church because it always
makes me feel guilty.'

'Tell me,' asked St Lynas, changing the subject.
'Do you think pain is a useful thing?'

After pondering the man said, 'I suppose it is,
for if we didn't hurt we wouldn't go to the doctor for a cure,
and we'd die.'

'Even if the cure made the pain hurt more for a bit?'
'Yes,' said the man, 'even then.'

'What were you saying about guilt?' asked St Lynas.

EXPERIENCE

A shop-keeper handed the pocket calculator to St Lynas
which came as a free gift with the duplicating paper he'd
bought.

'It does percentages, VAT returns, investment interest—all
sorts of things,' he told him.

'But we haven't any investments to add up!' St Lynas
protested,
'all our living is 100%, and we don't reclaim VAT.'

'It's pointless giving it to me.
It's just like someone who spends all his time trying to
define God, and hasn't any experience of him at all.'

DEDICATION

One of the brothers was unsettled.
He wasn't as quick or as gifted as the others, knew it,
and it depressed him so much he was thinking of leaving.

St Lynas called him into the garden one afternon, and after
a long chat, summed it up by saying:
'My dear friend, there are only two creatures
that can get to the top of a pyramid.
An eagle and a snail.'

THE HIGH GROUND

A man who had been very hurt by his neighbour came to
see St Lynas.
After listening to all that had happened, St Lynas asked:

'Do you want to be the same as your neighbour,
or better than he is?'
'Better, I suppose,' he answered.

'Well,' explained St Lynas, 'that's simple, though not easy.
If you treat him in the same way he's treated you, you'll be
on a level.
But if you forgive him, you'll have won the moral high
ground.'

OLD AGE

Chatting to one of the old men of the village over the hedge
one day, St Lynas asked how old he was.

'I ferget exactically,' the old man replied,
'but I'm certainly an octo-geranium!'

As St Lynas walked away chuckling, he explained to his
companion:
'That means that he's still growing. He's a colourful
character, he brings pleasure to those who meet him.
I wonder what he'll be like when he grows up?'

CAREFULNESS

One of the visitors was talking rather wildly one day,
when St Lynas told the story of the lady who hired a
chauffeur.

'How fast can you drive safely?' she asked one applicant.
'Oh, about 80 miles an hour,' he replied,
'the police don't worry about that.'
The second applicant said, 'just about 70 I suppose.'
The third said, 'I've never bothered to find out.'
'So she hired the third,' said St Lynas, 'wouldn't you?'

HUMILITY

St Lynas was treated with some rudeness by a visitor,
and his friends were astounded at the humble way he
accepted it.
'It doesn't matter,' he said evenly.

'There's nothing so soft as water,
but it wears down mountains.
It's the tigers and eagles of this world
which are the endangered species.
Not', he added with a sly smile,
'not the meek sheep like me!'

DRESS

St Lynas and the village atheist were sitting on a bench outside *The Old Bull*, trying to cure the dehydration of a hot day.
Taking a long pull of 'Old Peculiar', the atheist belched and said,
'I don't particularly want to go to heaven.'

'Why not?' asked St Lynas, being rather more modest with his lager.

'Well, how would I get my shirt on over my wings?' said the atheist.

'Shouldn't worry about that!' replied St Lynas. 'If I were you, I'd be more worried about how you're going to get your trousers on over your tail!'

RICHES

St Lynas was asked to speak to the local Rotary Club.
After a pleasant meal, he congratulated all the businessmen
on their social conscience, and the good work they did.

'You've all got good jobs, and I'm glad you have,' he said.
'for the money you earn helps you to do all these things.
But don't confuse this with how much you're worth.'

And he fixed them with a gimlet eye.
'When you get home to your families tonight,
look at them and ask yourself,
"How rich would I be if I lost all my money?"'

REVENGE

The village atheist was steaming!
'I'll get back at him!' he said.
'He won't get away with pulling this dirty trick on me, of
all people!'
he spluttered.

St Lynas walked up behind him and said mildly,
'I don't know who you're talking about, but I'd advise you
not to.
You see, you haven't got a yellow and black striped jersey.'

'What's that got to do with it?' the atheist shouted.
'Well,' explained St Lynas gently,
'you're a bee not a wasp, and when bees sting, they die!'

126

HOLIDAYS

Talking over a cup of tea after addressing a meeting in a church on the other side of the county, one of the ladies apologised for the minister of the church not being present.

'He's on holiday,' she explained,
'but he does seem to have been away a very long time!'

'My dear,' St Lynas said, 'don't complain.
If he's good, he deserves a nice long holiday.'

'And if he isn't, you deserve it.'

127

CONSPIRACY OF GOODNESS

Whenever St Lynas got off a bus, he always thanked the bus driver for his safe driving. When he was served in a shop, he was always politely grateful for their helpfulness.
He would habitually give a smiling 'good morning' to a gloomy person, and a conspiratorial wink to a very plain lady.

The brothers were amused at this, and asked him about it one day.

'I'm afraid it's a weakness of mine,' he said shamefacedly.
'You see, I know that what I do is going to rub off on the people those folk are going to meet later in the day.'

'I know it's an underhand thing to do.'
And with a bright smile he added
'But I think that being helpful and sneaky at the same time is a lot of fun!'

A DEVILISH TRICK

Having been to the supermarket in the village with one of the brothers, St Lynas was leaving with arms loaded with cartons of food for the following week.

After twenty yards he commented:
'It's on days like this that I really believe in the devil.'

'Why particularly days like this?' asked his friend.

'Well,' replied St Lynas, puffing with his load, 'who else would always tickle your nose when you've got your arms full?'

DELIGHT

A crowd of young children used the community for an
outing one Saturday.
St Lynas was in his element organising the games in the
garden, and telling them stories.

He also taught them a poem,
which at tea they recited for their parents in piping voices.

   'I'm glad the sky is painted blue
   And the earth is painted green,
   And such a lot of God's fresh air
   Is sandwiched in between.'

PLACEMENT

'Lord,' said St Lynas one fine day, 'I'm too comfortable!
I like my friends, I enjoy what I do, and I've got everything
I need, so it bothers me!'

'What on earth for?' asked God.

'Well, shouldn't I be struggling down in the slums,
or in an African village somewhere?'

'No,' replied God. 'You're most useful here,
which is why I arranged to put you here in the first place.
As soon as I made you, I saw that you might make a passable
saint—but a rotten martyr!'

PENSIONS

At the end of the Village Gala which had, for once,
been blessed with lovely weather,
St Lynas was driving home with the mini-bus fully loaded
with trestle tables and helpers.

As he waited at the traffic lights he sighed and said
contentedly, 'Well, that's one for my pension.'

'Pension?' asked one of the passengers.

'Yes,' replied St Lynas. 'It's been a great day,
and I'm saving all my good memories to live on when I
retire.'

FIRST IMPRESSIONS

One of the brothers was keen on photography and spent a
lot of time in one of the rooms making his prints.
He was also one of the most argumentative people in the
house.

'I appreciate that you're trying to come to your own
understanding of Christianity,' St Lynas said to him one
day as they were washing up together. 'But think of it in
photographic terms.'

'God's finger touching you is putting the picture invisibly
upon you, your belief develops it,
and your understanding fixes it to stop it fading away.'

'You can fix with your understanding as much as you like,
but without the picture in the first place—nothing!'

HINDSIGHT

St Lynas and the brothers were coming out of the park one
Saturday when they were button-holed by a man carrying
a text on a stick.

He went into great detail about the Latter Days,
and bolstered his evidence with figures from the Book of
Daniel and Revelation.

St Lynas listened politely and left as soon as he could.
Breathing a sigh of relief, the brothers asked him,
'Do you believe all that?'

'Reminds me,' said St Lynas,
'of the knight who rushed into the king's presence, and
shouted,
"My liege, the hundred years' war has just broken out."'

MARRIAGE

The village atheist and his wife were in the café with St
Lynas one day, when the man was called away to the phone.

'I hope he's not been any trouble to you,' the wife said to
St Lynas,
'he can be difficult sometimes.'

'Nothing I can't cope with, my dear,' replied St Lynas.
'And as for you, remember St Elisabeth of Castille.'

'Why her?' she asked with wide eyes.

'Well, she's the only woman I know who was made a saint
for living with her husband!'

CHRISTMAS

St Lynas arrived home weary after travelling 400 miles to attend a one-hour committee meeting in London.

'A long way to go just for that,' he commented to God.

'Ha! that's just what the angel choir said when they got back from Bethlehem,'
replied God.

'But think of the after-effects, lads, I told them—think of the after-effects!'

DOING GOOD

St Lynas and one of the brothers had a hectic day chasing around delivering and collecting things.

On the way home late at night they called at the Fish and Chip shop.
As they were eating in the minibus, St Lynas commented:

'You know, our Lord spent his time going about doing good. It strikes me that we settle too often for just "going about."'

SPIRITUALITY

One group of people couldn't get on with St Lynas
because they didn't think he was spiritual enough.

They belonged to the exclusive Christian group
who met in a small house opposite the Green, and one of
them, seeing St Lynas helping a stallholder to put up his
market stall one windy day, said as she passed:
'My dear man, why don't you look after your soul?'

'I'm afraid I'd quite forgotten I had one!' replied St Lynas,
good-humouredly.

She sniffed and walked on.

'Was that a good reply, Lord?' asked St Lynas.
'Don't waste time talking,' said God, 'tie that cover down quick.'

RELAXATION

One of St Lynas' habits was to sit at the door of the garden shed for half an hour every morning and feed the birds who grew surprisingly tame.

He didn't spend the time thinking, or doing, just 'being'. When he was asked about it once he said:

'I got the idea from a legend that St John used to have a tame partridge.
One day a huntsman passed and criticised him for not getting on with his work.
St John then asked him if he kept his bow bent and fully strung all the time.
"Of course not, it would then be useless," the huntsman said.
"Quite," said St John.'

EXISTENCE OF GOD

The village atheist was feeling in an argumentative mood.
'I don't believe God exists!' he challenged St Lynas.

'Did your parents?' asked St Lynas.
'They didn't believe in him either,' he replied.

'No, I meant did they exist?' said St Lynas.
'Of course they existed, you chump,' said the atheist,
'otherwise I wouldn't be here!'

'Well?' replied St Lynas.

GOSPEL

Dishing up the lunch one day, St Lynas said to everyone
with a flourish,
'Today, fish fingers!'

But one of the brothers said:
'The Consumer Guide says that they're only 50% fish,
the rest is water, crumbs and additives.'

'Ah well, I suppose we can live with that,' St Lynas replied,
fixing them with a beady eye,
'but don't settle for a filleted and diluted Gospel—
it wouldn't feed the soul of a tom-tit!'

THE IMPOSSIBLE

An old friend of St Lynas came to visit him,
and they sat for a long time in the lounge reminiscing.

'What a place you've set up here!' his friend said.
'When I think how you started, it's incredible!'

'Ah, the situation here is different from the business world,
for instance,' said St Lynas.

'With you, things can be serious without being impossible.
Here, in a Christian environment,
things are always impossible without being serious.'

EXUBERANCE

One morning St Lynas felt exuberantly full of life.
He vaulted over the five-bar gate, ran down the field, sat on
a tree stump, and had just enough puff left to shout 'Wheee!'

'You feeling all right, Lynas?' asked God.

'Bright as a button!' answered St Lynas, 'what a wonderful
day!
Surely you know how I feel, Lord?'

'Indeed I do,' replied God smiling.
'Once it resulted in the duck-billed platypus,
and another time it was the mandarin duck!'

SACRIFICE

A high pressure evangelist visited the community one day,
to apologise for not having the time for a mission in the
village.
St Lynas' friends were thrilled by him,
and after he'd gone back to his large wealthy church,
asked St Lynas what he thought.

'I always think it's strange,' he replied,
'how the people who are so keen to shed their last drop of
blood for the faith, are so very particular where they shed
the *first* drop.'

¹44
THE BIBLE

One new brother asked St Lynas how he should study the Bible.
'Get a modern version, and read whole books at a time', said St Lynas.

'But the most important thing is to look for the questions,' he went on.
'There is a big question in your heart, my friend—it's struggling to get out.
You'll find it in your reading.'

'You might even . . .' St Lynas smiled,
'get a glimpse of an answer!'

¹45
WORK

Out in the garden one evening St Lynas was energetically spraying the roses with soapy water, and singing loudly an old hymn no-one else knew.

'Most important job, this!' he explained to the brother who was cutting the lawn. 'They need a clean-up in July.'
And he quoted the limerick:

    The indolent vicar of Bray
    Let his lovely red roses decay.
    His wife, more alert,
    Bought a powerful squirt,
    And said to her spouse, 'Let us spray'.

146

THE UPSIDE DOWN JESUS

The brothers were doing a project which, like the old Balloon Game, involved deciding who of a list of people would qualify for treatment on a kidney machine.

They ended up deciding to save those who were most use to society—the greatest good to the greatest number.

St Lynas was wary of the conclusion.
'I agree with you, but I have the uncomfortable feeling that those are not the ones Jesus would save,' he commented.

'But it's precisely the list the Pharisees would have.'

147

THE BURDEN

One of St Lynas' friends was in constant pain from a cancer.

'I know it's a stupid question, Lord,' said St Lynas, 'but why him?
He's never hurt a fly!'

'That's not you being ridiculous, Lynas, but your hurt,' replied God.
'There's a certain amount of suffering in the world, and you all have to carry a bit.'

'And don't forget,' God continued,
'I arranged for my son to carry most of it for you!'

THE BALD TRUTH

St Lynas was sitting in the kitchen while one of the
community was trying to cut his hair.

He'd mounted a search for the hairs on the top and was
now tackling the mop on the back. 'Faith,' he pontificated,
'is going to the chemists and buying hair-restorer and a comb
at the same time!'

'Nonsense!' said St Lynas, shaking his head and putting his
ears at grave risk from the scissors.
'Faith is saying "Thank God I don't have to buy combs any
more!"'

BEING OLD

Talking to a group of pensioners in the village hall one day,
St Lynas tried to cheer them up.

'Yes, I know we're known as "wrinklies" and "crumblies",
he told them, 'and speaking for myself"
I'm getting rapidly near to my "sell-by date".'

'But it doesn't matter how old you are—
it's *how* you are *old* that counts!'

THE CHRISTIAN BATTLE

Walking down the road with an old friend who had a small business, they discussed the difficulty of living a Christian life in the modern cut-throat world.

'It's tough!' the friend said, 'all sorts of little corruptions and a lack of integrity everywhere.'

'Yes, I know,' said St Lynas. 'But you must be true to yourself and your Lord.'

'Don't forget that, like all explorers, if you want to reach the source, you must swim against the flow.'

151

SELFISHNESS

St Lynas was showing a party of prosperous businessmen around the estate.
He got on with them very well. 'Money's very useful,' he said,
'when it's combined with generosity. It's a killer when it isn't!'

'There's an old story of a rich man who fell into the river. Lots of people gathered around and said, "Give us your hand."
But he couldn't reach out in his panic.

If only they'd remembered what kind of rich man he was, and said "*Take* this rope" he wouldn't have drowned.'

PRAYERFULNESS

Sitting at the back of the church, and looking at the people receiving communion, one thing St Lynas could not escape was seeing the soles of everyone's shoes.

'Some good praying people here today,'
he whispered to the brother next to him.

'How can you know that?' the brother whispered back.

'Look at those well-worn shoes,' said St Lynas.
'You can identifiy the people who pray far more accurately from their shoes than their knees.'

153
WRONG!

One of St Lynas' biggest gaffes occurred at the local Cottage Hospital.

He had a look at the Sister's list of patients, in her absence, and noticed that they were an unusual religious mixture, 15 M, 3 CE, and 1 RC.

After he'd visited all the Methodists, Church of England, and Roman Catholics, he remarked on the strange mixture of denominations.

'Denominations be blowed!' said the Sister, 'that's the dinner order—15 Moussaka, 3 Curried Eggs, and one Roast Chicken!'

154
LOVE MY DOG

The atheist was walking along Market Street with his new puppy, when St Lynas stopped to admire it.

'Very nice,' he said, 'a lovely King Charles, cost quite a packet I expect.'

'£150—a pedigree as long as your arm! The best bred dog in the village!' said the atheist.

'Just one thing you need to remember,' commented St Lynas as he patted the puppy. 'Money can buy a dog, but money can't make its tail wag!'

155
ACTIONS

St Lynas and one of the brothers went round to the house
to see a lady after her husband had died.

Sitting down and putting his hand on hers, he asked, 'What
happened?'
They then sat and said nothing for an hour while she
expressed her grief.

Going home, the brother said, 'I had all sorts of things to say
but didn't get a chance.'

'Goodness me!' replied St Lynas. 'Don't you see, by just
being there, in keeping my hand on hers, we said more
than an ocean of words.
The deepest things can only be expressed by actions, not
speech.'

156
A FAITH TO FIT

Waiting to cross the road, St Lynas chatted to the lollipop
man, whom he knew was a regular chapelgoer.
'Tell me Fred,' asked St Lynas, 'why do you keep going to
chapel?
Indeed, why are you a Christian at all?'
'Because it suits me!' replied the lollipop man.

'Now there's a wise man,' said St Lynas to his companion
as they crossed the road.

'When the shoe fits the feet are forgotten,
when the collar fits the neck is taken for granted.
And when the faith suits us, we can get on with living!'

LOVE AND MARRIAGE

When one of the brothers married,
he asked St Lynas to preach the sermon at the wedding.
What St Lynas said was this:

'Love is the most powerful and the weakest thing there is.
Its strength is that alone it can open the door
of that most invulnerable of fortresses, the heart of someone
else.
Its weakness is that it can only operate by consent.

You two have "consented together", so the weakness is
overcome.
I pray that the strength of love, yours and God's, may be
always between you.'

158

JUDGEMENT

The local priest, who had a reputation for hellfire preaching,
was friendly to St Lynas, but disagreed with his tolerant views.

'You've got to draw the line somewhere!' he exclaimed with
emphasis.
'We've got to make clear to the community that there is
such a thing as right and wrong.'

'You mean,' said St Lynas, 'that just as we should express
God's love, we should also express God's judgement.'
'Put in a nutshell!' said the priest.

'Ah, but you forget,' said St Lynas quietly,
'that Our Lord commanded us to love, and told us *not* to
judge!'

SINNERS ALL

The sandwich-board man had a different text.
**The price of a virtuous woman is above rubies.
(Proverbs 31:10)**

Feeling skittish, St Lynas remarked to him as he passed:
'With the 700 wives and 300 concubines Solomon had, he
should have known!'
'Ah, that was before he was converted!' said the man.

And fixing St Lynas with hypnotic goodwill he continued,
'I was once a sinner like you!'

As he walked away with his companion St Lynas said 'You
know, like a broken clock's right twice a day, he's probably
correct about THAT!'

TEACHING

St Lynas was chatting with a group of rebellious young
college students one day, who decried the moral standards
of the past.

So St Lynas drew an 'a' on some paper, and asked them
what it was.
'A' they said.

He did the same with a 'b'. 'It's a "B,"' they replied.

'How do you know that?' asked St Lynas.
'Because we were taught it,' they answered.
'Well?' countered St Lynas.

GOD IN ONE

St Lynas was persuaded to play a game of golf with some friends, a game at which he was hopeless.

He took an almighty swipe at the ball, which sailed into the middle distance, hit a tree, rebounded down a dozen branches and fell straight into a rabbit hole.

'My God!' exclaimed St Lynas 'a hole in one!'

'It's nice to be appreciated,' confessed God. 'I couldn't resist it!'

EQUAL IN GOD'S LOVE

One of the brothers asked St Lynas one day how much the
two cats ate.
'Maggie eats two platefuls a day, and so does Edie', was the
reply.

'Where do they sleep during the day?' he was then asked.
'Maggie's favourite place is the stone flag in the shrubbery,'
St Lynas replied,
'Edie sleeps there too.'

'Why do you always differentiate between the two?' asked
the brother.
'Well, Maggie belongs to me.'

'Who does Edie belong to then?' asked the puzzled brother.
'She belongs to me too,' said St Lynas, quietly.

'They're not equal in my *sight*, but they're equal in my *love*.'

163

THE APOSTLE

The brothers were startled one day when over breakfast St
Lynas, who had been quietly reading his letters, suddenly
stood up, rattled his spoon against his dish and announced:

'A bible reading, friends! It comes from the Acts of the
Apostles, chapter one million and twenty seven.'

He then read out the letter from his friend in a mission in
Nepal.

DOUBTS

St Lynas and one of the brothers were doing some weeding
in the shrubbery opposite the house one day, and chatting
as they hoed.

'I get quite a lot of doubts these days,' said the brother,
'and I'm ashamed of them.'

St Lynas leaned on his hoe with a sigh.
'I'd willingly excommunicate the people who've told you
that doubts come from the devil,' he said. 'They don't!'

'God sends them. Like biscuit crumbs in bed,
they stop our faith going to sleep!'

HOPE

'How on earth can you always be so hopeful?' challenged
the village atheist, one day as he caught St Lynas going into
the vet's.
'The world's going to the devil!'

'Well, passing over the fact that you should know,' said St
Lynas,
'I reckon that on the whole there's more justice than
injustice, more good marriages than divorces, more loved
children than neglected ones, and more happiness than
sorrow.'

'I also reckon,' continued St Lynas,
'that it'll be the same tomorrow—thank God.'

BELONGING

One early morning St Lynas was wandering round the
garden with a lady visitor who was also an early riser.

They came across a large spider's web, glistening with dew.
'How beautiful!' said the lady.

'Reminds me of John Donne,' said St Lynas, '"the bells toll
for you" bit.'
'Why that?' she asked.

'Well, touch any one of the strands of that web,' explained
St Lynas,
'and the whole thing, every other strand, its whole world
quivers!'

167

SIN

'I came across a fellow cursing you up hill and down dale,'
said St Lynas to God, while feeding the chickens one
morning.
'Really?' said God, who was clearly not very interested.
'Ah well, my back's broad!'

'He's the fellow who was in court for battering his wife and
children,' explained St Lynas.

'What?' said God very loudly, 'that's serious!'
'Wait a minute, Lord,' said St Lynas,
'are you implying that a sin against human beings is more
sinful than a sin against you?'

'Of course! It's twice as bad!' said God with great emphasis,
'what else could it be?'

168

BENEVOLENCE

The brothers all went with St Lynas to a charity concert.
The standard was poor, the seats uncomfortable,
and the main singer appalling.
He put the smallest coin he had in the collection.

'You didn't give much!' they said to him afterwards,
as they were walking home.
'On the contrary,' he said,
'I gave the most painful things I could—forgiving and
thanksgiving!'

GENEROSITY

Talking with a colleague about a brother who was a bit
selfish, St Lynas said,
'Don't worry, he'll grow out of it!'

'I wish I could be so confident,' said his friend.

'Well, remember this,' responded St Lynas.
'As babies we are born with our hands clenched,
at the start of life we grab everything we can.
But then as we grow older most of us grow more generous,
and we die, having given lots away, with our hands open.'

ASPIRATION

Sitting with St Lynas on the park bench overlooking the
flower beds, the village atheist questioned the need for
religion.
'Why not just be content with being human,'
he said, 'why always strain after being something better?'

'You're in the worst place for arguing that!' chuckled St
Lynas.

'Look at all those flowers, the grass and the trees.
Every single thing exists because it resisted the force of
gravity, and tried to reach the light it saw.'

BIGOTRY

St Lynas was chatting with the old man (the octo-geranium)
who said of a neighbour up the lane:

'Ee's a lad, that one, at least he were in his younger days—
he married three women. Oi reckon that's bigotry!'

'No, no,' said St Lynas, smiling broadly.
'Two wives is bigotry—three is trigonometry!'

THE EXTRA TOUCH

When St Lynas gives a food parcel to someone in need who
calls, he always adds a flower in summer, and a bar of
chocolate in winter.

When one of the brothers asked him why, he explained:

'When God gave us air, he added summer breezes;
when he gave us light, he added gorgeous sunsets;
when he made water, he threw in rippling streams.

Hence the flower—it's not so much duty, as love.'

173

CASTING CARE ON THE LORD

In St Lynas' room there is a big ancient safe. It is full of
shoe boxes, each with the name of someone in the house,
and most of them empty.

When visitors come, even for just a week, they are given a
box, and told to put all the things that worry and trouble
them in it, before it is locked in the safe.

'Just ask when you want to get them out again,' says St Lynas.
But strangely, few of them ever do.

174

RELIGION

Sitting in a car crossing the great Humber bridge one day,
St Lynas remarked,
'What a religious thing this is! I hope someone blessed it
when it was opened.'

'Religious?' incredulously asked his companion who
travelled over it routinely every day.

'Yes,' said St Lynas. 'It would be easy to shelter under it,
to admire or criticise the way it's made, and take pretty
photographs of it at sunset, but not to travel over it.'

'Just like people who forget that the Christian Faith is a
bridge too.'

RECOGNISING GOD

St Lynas' priorities were sometimes unexpected.
For instance one day he asked the brothers,
'Who is the greater villain, a smash-and-grab robber or a
sneakthief?'

'Both about equally rotten,' said the brothers.

'Oh no,' said St Lynas. 'The sneakthief is the worse.'

'You see the smash and grab man knows he's going against
God, and defies him. The sneakthief acts secretly and thinks
God's eye isn't on him.

That's much worse.'

176

AWE

St Lynas had just treated himself to a secondhand pair of binoculars, and that night spent a couple of hours outside looking at the stars.

'Lord, how many are there?' asked St Lynas.
'Wrong question,' said God.
'Are you out there or inside me?' asked St Lynas.
'Wrong question again,' said God.

'Is there a right question?' asked St Lynas.
'No,' said God, with finality, 'not in this case.'

'But Lord, look at all these stars—wow!'
'Ah,' said God, 'now you're getting warmer.'

177

WORRY

St Lynas doesn't like people being worried. 'Practical atheism' he calls it.
Given half a chance he quotes the rhyme by Taylor Smith:

  'The worried cow would have lived 'til now
  If she had saved her breath;
  But she feared her hay
  Wouldn't last all day,
  And she mooed herself to death.'

PARADOX

St Lynas was asked to attend a Lent House Group,
which included people of many different denominations.

The discussion at one point got into deep theological waters,
and became quite heated.

'Calm down!' said St Lynas. 'What we have to remember
is that there are dozens of different ways of explaining the
mysteries of God, and all of them are right!'

But he continued, 'And all of them are wrong, as well!'

DAWN

One spring St Lynas, having been reading until late, was woken up by the birds singing 'Aida' at half past three outside his window.

'Lord,' said St Lynas,
'why did you invent a time like half past three in the morning?'

'Well,' replied God, 'I had to fill in the gap between supper and breakfast somehow!'

'Then why did you get these pesky birds up so early?'
'I didn't,' said God.
'It was such a nice morning, they thought of it themselves.'

KNOWING GOD

The brothers were arguing one day about what God was like.
The youngest one, of course, knew most,
and went into great detail about God's nature.

Without comment, St Lynas went and fetched a hammer
and a six inch nail, which he noisily drove into the
mantelpiece.
'What on earth are you doing?' they asked.
'Nailing God down to this mantelpiece,' he replied.
'But you can't do that!' they said.

'Really?' replied St Lynas.
'Hmmm—come to think of it, it didn't work the last time
they tried to nail him down either.'

COMMONSENSE

One day St Lynas had a problem. He'd changed the oil in
the minibus, and didn't know what to do with the can of
waste oil.
So over lunch he sat quietly thinking.

Then he wrapped the can in gift paper,
tied it with ribbon, and drove into the village.

Parking the minibus on the roadside, he carefully locked
the doors, but opened the passenger window, leaving the
parcel on the seat.

When he got back from the post office, the oil had gone.

CREATIVE LOVE

After supper one night they were talking about creation,
and St Lynas told this story:

'When God was thinking about making Adam and Eve,
a deputation of angels asked to see him.
The Angel of Peace pleaded with God not to do it.
"Think of their descendants, they'll shed blood, torture and
kill."
The Angel of Joy also said
"Don't do it, they'll cause aeons of misery."
But the Angel of Love threw himself at God's feet
and with tears said, "Your will be done."
And as a reward for his understanding
God sent the Angel of Love to be with mankind in the world.'

PREACHING

A street corner preacher was accompanied by his dog
who howled all the time he was preaching.

St Lynas saw this and walked away chuckling.

'You see,' he explained to his friends,
'like can only speak to like.
If the dog really feels called to preach,
he should preach to the other dogs.'

184

CRITICISM

One of the brothers was a bit touchy,
and couldn't take even kindly, constructive criticism very
well.

One day St Lynas talked to him about it,
and about how everyone finds the process painful but
helpful.

'I've got just the thing to show you,' said St Lynas,
rooting through a cardboard carton in the corner.
He opened a brown envelope and showed the lad what
looked like a small pebble.

'That's a rough diamond given to me by an old friend,' he
said.
'All it needs to turn it into a sparkling gem is a careful
grinding down, but I can't bring myself to do it!'

IN THE BOOK

St Lynas was in a grumpy mood having had an argument
with a man about the meaning of one passage of the Bible.
Nothing St Lynas could say would shift him from his over-
literal interpretation.

'Lord!' said St Lynas in despair, 'why don't you speak to
him loud and clear?
You've got the thunderous voice to convince him!'

'Already done it, and it didn't do any good,' replied God.
'He said the voice couldn't be mine because it wasn't "in
the book!"'

STARTING POINT

'Lord, that atheist friend of mine is a nice enough fellow
really, why can't I get through to him?' prayed St Lynas
that night.

'I don't know, has to do with his upbringing I suppose,'
replied God.
'But surely you can do *something*!' pleaded St Lynas.

'Force wouldn't get us anywhere.
I'm already sending him all the stimuli I send you.
The trouble is he misinterprets them all!' said God.

'Tell you what, Lynas, seeing as you are very concerned,
I'll send him my best starter kit—a lump in the throat at a
moment of beauty or pain!'

REALISM

There are two larders in the house, one for the community use, and the other filled with food to give away.

The 'Poverty Pantry' is stocked by local churches who collect tins and packets at harvest time.

St Lynas rarely gives money.
'It usually ends at the pub or the betting shop!' he says.

'But I'd love to see them getting sozzled on prune juice, or putting two cans of beans on the favourite at Goodwood!'

ANTIDULLDOTE

Living in the community was never dull. St Lynas was always thinking of, or doing unusual things, which had everyone wondering 'whatever next?'

He did it deliberately, and as justification quoted this limerick:

'There was a young monk of Siberia,
Whose existence grew drearier and drearier,
Till he burst from his cell
With a hell of a yell
And eloped with the Mother Superior.'

THE TOUCH

St Lynas and the village atheist were walking down the road
after a moving concert in the village hall, and talking
seriously about spirituality.

St Lynas agreed that there was such a thing as 'a
spirituality of atheism',
and the atheist agreed that he'd been touched by a sense of
mystery.
'We both feel the same paradox and mystery,' said St Lynas.
'The difference is that you feel it as a static strangeness—
while I hear it as a call to pilgrimage.'

'I don't know why,' continued St Lynas,
'but I feel a tap on the shoulder and hear a voice saying
"Follow me".'
'God help me!' he added, with agonising seriousness,
'I can't see why you don't!'

SAINTLINESS

There is a simple conspiracy among the people in the
community.
They all refer to him as Saint Lynas, but never, ever to his
face.
Actually, among friends he much prefers to be called 'Pop'.

For, in their growing understanding of spiritual things
they see that he would heartily deny any virtue or wisdom
at all.

In fact, the topsy-turvy truth is that people who would
accept the title 'saint' are never worthy of it.

And a person like St Lynas, who would merit the title,
would be the last person in the world to see himself as one.

Index